A play by
Julia Donaldson

Yellow
Stockings

Illustrations by
Andrew Oliver

C000144721

Introduction

The Globe Theatre was in Southwark, across the River Thames from London Town. William Shakespeare wrote many of the plays performed there, and acted in them as well. *Twelfth Night* was probably written in 1601, towards the end of Queen Elizabeth's reign.

In the 1990s the Globe Theatre was rebuilt. It reopened in 1997.

Pip Fleet
A boy actor, aged 13

Annie Fleet
His twin sister, a seamstress

Mistress Fleet
Their mother, a tailor

An apothecary
A man who prepares and sells medicines

Sir Perry
A gentleman who is very concerned about his clothes and appearance, a "fop"

A fruit-seller

3

Scene One *A London street.*

Fruit-seller   Fine apples, apples fine!
A farthing for four, a ha-penny for nine.

Enter Pip.

Pip   I'll have nine. But let me taste one first.

Fruit-seller   *(suspiciously)* Let's see your ha-penny then.

Pip   Why? Don't you trust me?

Fruit-seller   I never trust a schoolboy.

Pip   I'm not a schoolboy. I'm an actor. You
sell your apples at the Globe Theatre,
don't you? Didn't you see me in last
week's tragedy? I was the girl who
drowned herself.

Fruit-seller So you were, and I nearly drowned too – in my own tears! Go on then, taste an apple, but don't make me cry like that again.

Pip I won't. The next play's a comedy. It's called *Twelfth Night*. I'm going to be the main character. She's called Viola.

Fruit-seller Do you always act as a girl?

Pip Usually. It makes my sister furious. She'd love to be on the stage herself. She doesn't think it's fair that girls aren't allowed to.

Fruit-seller I hope you don't drown yourself in this play.

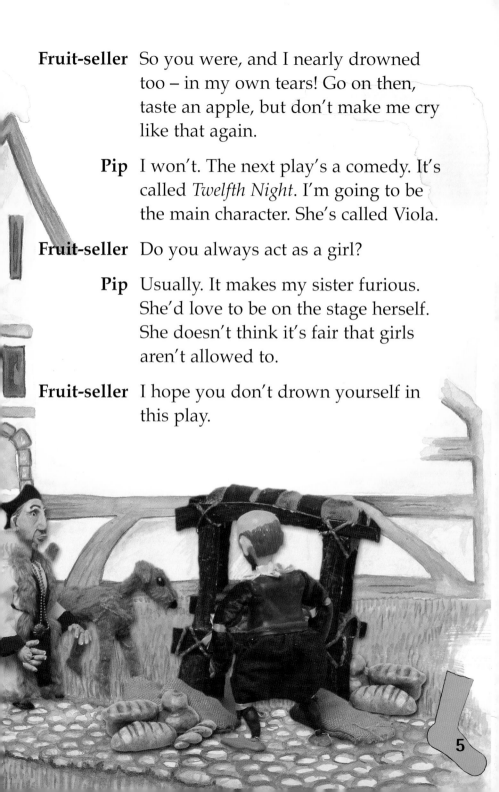

Pip No. I do get shipwrecked, but I end up on an island.

Fruit-seller You're a good swimmer then?

Pip Viola is. I'm not. To tell the truth, I can't swim!

Fruit-seller You're good at eating apples, though.

Pip Yes. That was very tasty.

Fruit-seller Do you still want nine?

Pip Well, there's just one problem. I don't have a ha-penny.

Fruit-seller I knew it all along! Be off with you!

Pip I'll see you at the Globe! And thanks for the apple! *(He runs off.)*

Scene Two *A tailor's shop.*

Enter Mistress Fleet.

Ms Fleet Annie! Annie!

Enter Annie, knitting a pair of bright yellow stockings.

Annie What is it, Mother?

Ms Fleet Haven't you finished those stockings for the play yet?

Annie I nearly have. What a horrible yellow!

6

No one in their right mind would want to wear them.

Ms Fleet Well, speed up. You know Pip's promised to take all the costumes across to the Globe in the boat this afternoon. *(There is the ting of the shop bell.)* Maybe this is him now. Oh no! It's Sir Perry.

Sir Perry Good morning, Mistress Fleet. Is my doublet ready?

Ms Fleet Yes, Sir Perry. Here it is.

Sir Perry Very good, very good – but I'm not so sure now about the sleeves. I fancy those

	turned-back cuffs are going out of fashion. Several of the gentlemen at court are wearing wrist ruffs. Pray make me a pair of wrist ruffs, Mistress Fleet.
Ms Fleet	Very well, Sir Perry. What colour?
Sir Perry	Let me think ... yellow. A bright yellow, a dazzling yellow, a yellow like ... like that pair of stockings your girl is knitting! In fact, I'll take the stockings too. They should turn a few heads at court.
Ms Fleet	I'm sorry, Sir, but those stockings are for one of the actors in Mr Shakespeare's new play.
Sir Perry	Then knit me an identical pair. And make sure they're ready in time for the play.
Ms Fleet	Are you going to see it, then?
Sir Perry	Of course! I never miss a new play. I caused quite a stir at the last one in my crimson satin cloak. I fancy more eyes were on me than on the actors! Good morning, Mistress Fleet. *(He exits.)*
Annie	Oh no! Not another pair of yellow stockings! I can't bear it!

Ms Fleet Stop moaning, Annie – it's all good business. Now, mind the shop while I go and buy some more yellow silk.

She exits and Pip enters.

Pip *(quoting from the play)* "What country, friends, is this?"

Annie *(scornfully)* Brilliant, you've learnt your first line!

Pip Wrong reply – you're supposed to say "It is Illyria, Lady."

Annie I wish it really was Illyria. Then I could be having impossible adventures instead of knitting awful stockings.

Pip What do you mean, impossible adventures? Are you criticising Mr Shakespeare's play?

Annie Well, it's all a bit unlikely, isn't it? Viola getting shipwrecked and then disguising herself as a man and fooling everyone! You're not telling me that could happen in real life?

Pip *(offended)* I don't see why not.

9

Annie And then her twin brother turning up on the same island and everyone mistaking one for the other.

Pip What's wrong with that?

Annie Oh, come on, Pip! We're twins but no one ever thinks I'm you.

Pip Maybe if you wore my clothes they would.

Annie I don't think so, somehow.

Pip You're just in a bad mood. Why don't you test me on my lines? Let's do the scene where Viola meets Lady Olivia.

He hands Annie his lines.

Annie All right then. I know, I'll wear Lady Olivia's veil! Here it is. *(She picks up a veil from the top of a pile of costumes and covers her face with it.)* Well, go on, say your first line.

Pip *(acting Viola)* "The honourable ... the honourable ..."

Annie *(prompting him)* "The honourable lady of the house, which is she?"

Pip Hey! I'm supposed to say that.

Annie I know; I was just prompting you. Honestly, Pip, I think I know these lines better than you do!

Enter Mistress Fleet.

Ms Fleet Annie, stop prancing around with that veil. You know it's for the play.

Annie I'm just testing Pip on his lines.

Ms Fleet Haven't you learnt them yet, Pip?
You're leaving it a bit late in the day.

Pip Well, what about
your costumes? They
don't seem to be ready.
Annie's still knitting
those yellow stockings.

Annie It's your fault for
making me test you on
your lines. Anyway,
I'm on the last row. I'll
have finished by the time you've
loaded the other clothes into the boat.

Ms Fleet Can you manage them all, Pip?

Pip I'll have to, won't I?

*He glares at Annie, who is still knitting, and picks up an
armful of clothes. As they exit, the apothecary enters,
carrying a tray of medicines.*

Apothecary Business is busy, I see.

Ms Fleet Yes. We've been making costumes for
the new play at the Globe Theatre. My
son is acting in it, too.

Apothecary I'm sorry to hear that. The playhouse is
the haunt of the devil.

Ms Fleet What can I do for you, Sir?

Apothecary The strap from my tray of medicines has snapped. Can you make me a new one?

Ms Fleet Certainly, Sir. What colour would you like?

Apothecary Something plain and dark.

Ms Fleet How about this brown braid? If you empty your tray I can fix it for you while you wait.

Apothecary Thank you. You seem to be a sensible woman in spite of your unfortunate connection with the theatre.

Ms Fleet Is it just medicines you sell? No sweets or face powder?

Apothecary Certainly not. Those are the wares of the devil.

Enter Annie, in a panic.

Annie Mother, Mother! Something terrible has happened! Pip started rowing before I'd finished the stockings.

13

Ms Fleet   That's not so terrible.

Annie   No, but then I finished them and threw them to him, and he lost his balance and toppled into the river!

Apothecary   Heaven preserve him!

Ms Fleet   Quick! Can you swim, Sir?

Apothecary   Er ...

Annie   It's all right. He's been rescued by a young woman, a fruit-seller. She jumped in and saved him.

Ms Fleet   Thank goodness for that!

Annie   Here they come now.

Enter Pip and the fruit-seller, both wet. Pip is sneezing.

Ms Fleet   Oh, Pip! A thousand thanks, young woman! Oh, you're both soaking! Annie, fetch some towels!

Apothecary I have some lily root here, Mistress Fleet. If you boil it in white wine it is a cure for the shivering fits.

Fruit-seller I think some dry clothes might be a better cure.

Ms Fleet Let's all go into the back room. The fire is lit in there. Annie, bring some clothes through.

Annie Yes, Mother. And then I'll row the costumes across.

They all go into the back room. Annie takes in some clothes and the apothecary takes in his tray.

Apothecary *(as he goes out)* It is a warning from Heaven. The boy should leave the theatre!

Scene Three *Pip's bedroom, a few days later.*

Enter Mistress Fleet, Annie and the apothecary.

Ms Fleet The apothecary has come to see you again, Pip.

Apothecary Let me feel your brow. Hmmm, there is still some fever.

Annie It's not the plague, is it, Sir? Please say it's not the plague.

Apothecary No, there are no swellings. God willing, the boy has been spared. Keep giving him the boiled lily root, and some of this onion and vinegar drink. That should bring the fever down. And above all, keep him away from the theatre!

Pip *(whispering)* Will the drink bring my voice back?

Apothecary Yes, in a week or so. Some oil and gunpowder mixture might bring it back even sooner.

Pip How soon?

Apothecary A couple of days perhaps.

Pip But the play is due to open this afternoon!

Ms Fleet That's too bad, Pip. They'll just have to find someone else to play Viola.

Apothecary In my opinion, they would do better to close down the theatre.

Ms Fleet Thank you for all your help, Sir. I'll see you out.

Exit Ms Fleet and the apothecary.

Pip *(still whispering)* I must go to the theatre! I'll be thrown out of the play if I don't. I'm already in trouble for being late learning my lines.

Annie Pip ... I know your lines. I've tested you on them often enough.

Pip Stop boasting, Annie.

Annie I'm not boasting. I've got an idea. You know you said people might think I was you if I wore your clothes? Well, why don't I give it a try?

Pip What, you act Viola? You must be joking.

Annie No, I'm not. Leave it to me, Pip.

Scene Four *The Globe Theatre.*

The first performance of Twelfth Night *is just ending. The fruit-seller and Sir Perry are among the audience.*

Annie *(singing on the stage)*
A great while ago the world begun,
With hey ho, the wind and the rain,
But that's all one, our play is done,
And we'll strive to please you every day.

Everyone claps. She bows and exits.

Fruit-seller   Did you enjoy the play, Sir Perry?

Sir Perry   To tell the truth, I preferred the last one.

Fruit-seller   Viola was good, though, wasn't she? He, I mean. He was really convincing.

Sir Perry   Ah yes, young Pip Fleet.

Fruit-seller   You could have sworn she was a real woman – even though she was pretending to be a man for most of the play.

Sir Perry   I know the Fleet family well. They made my doublet. I expect you've been admiring the wrist ruffs?

Fruit-seller Sorry, Sir Perry, I was too busy watching the play. Wasn't that idiot in those awful yellow stockings funny?

Sir Perry Not particularly.

Fruit-seller The way he was strutting around – he really thought Lady Olivia fancied him. Yellow stockings! I nearly died laughing!

Sir Perry I can't say I saw the joke.

Enter Ms Fleet.

Fruit-seller Good afternoon, Mistress Fleet. You must be proud of Pip.

Ms Fleet Yes, I am.

Fruit-seller   Well, I must try to sell the rest of my apples. Fine apples, apples fine. A farthing for four, a ha-penny for nine.

She exits.

Ms Fleet   Wasn't it a wonderful play, Sir Perry?

Sir Perry   Personally, I thought it was much too full of impossible adventures.

Ms Fleet   What do you mean, impossible adventures?

Sir Perry   Twins, shipwrecks, rescues ... too unlikely for words.

Ms Fleet   I'm not so sure about that.

Sir Perry And then, in real life, no one would mistake a woman for a man like that, would they? I certainly wouldn't.

Ms Fleet If you say so, Sir Perry.

Sir Perry By the by, did your daughter come to the play, Mistress Fleet? I would like a word with her.

Ms Fleet Er … no, she was too busy sewing.

Sir Perry A pity. A pity.

Ms Fleet Can I give her a message?

Sir Perry Yes. I would like another pair of stockings.

Ms Fleet *(trying not to laugh)* Very well. Yellow ones again, Sir Perry?

Sir Perry No. Strangely enough, these yellow stockings are no longer to my liking. Pray ask your daughter to knit me some violet stockings.

READY, STEADY, ACT!

Now that you have read this play it's time to act it out.

CHOOSING THE PARTS

Choose who will play each part.
- Pip is chatty and cheeky. He loses his voice.
- Annie is his twin. She sings well and she is a bit jealous of Pip.
- Ms Fleet is keen to please and cares for the twins.
- The fruit-seller has a loud voice and maybe a Cockney accent.
- The apothecary is serious and hates the theatre.
- Sir Perry is vain and foolish.

Who in your cast would be best at these roles? Read sections of the play, taking turns at different parts.

SETTING THE SCENE

The action is set in Elizabethan times and there are four scenes. One way to show this is to have signs saying, 'A London Street' and so on. You could begin your play with a street scene with sound effects, music and voices of market traders.

Did you know…?
Did you know that the character in *Twelfth Night* who actually wears yellow stockings is called Malvolio?

23

WHAT YOU WILL NEED

Costumes and Props

There are all sorts of ways to show that you are in Elizabethan times.

- You can make cloaks using lengths of cloth.
- Boys can tuck their trousers into long socks. Girls can wear long, full skirts and aprons.
- Find some waistcoats and hats.
- Sir Perry should look silly.

Make a props list; find or make what you need.

SPEAKING AND MOVING

Speaking

How will Pip speak when he is saying lines from his play? Make him sound like a real actor. Later, he has to speak in a whisper, but he still needs to be heard. Can you make Sir Perry sound like a rich twit?

Moving

Practise walking as if you are soaking wet like Pip.

What next?

Now you have performed this play why not …

- read the story of Shakespeare's *Twelfth Night*
- research some more cold remedies.